ENKI BILAL

THE WOMAN TRAP

TITAN BOOKS

LONDON

Other books by Enki Bilal: -
Gods in Chaos
The Town Which Did Not Exist (Coming soon)
Phalanxes of the Black Order (Coming soon)
The Hunting Party (Coming soon)

Other Titan Books in this series:
The Gardens of Aedena by Moebius
Joe's Bar by Carlos Sampayo and José Muñoz
The Last Voyage of Sindbad by Jan Strnad and Richard Corben
The Long Voyage and other Science Fiction Stories
by Moebius
The Magician's Wife by Jerome Charyn and Francois Boucq
Pharagonesia by Moebius

THE WOMAN TRAP
ISBN: 1 85286 076 6

Written and illustrated by Enki Bilal

Published by
Titan Books Ltd,
58 St Giles High St,
London WC2H 8LH.
First Titan Edition, August 1988
10 9 8 7 6 5 4 3 2 1

British edition by arrangement with
Catalan Communications, 43 East 19th Street, New York,
N.Y. 10003, USA

Copyright © Dargaud Editeur, Paris, by Bilal.
Translation by Tom Leighton.
Edited by Bernd Metz.
Designed by Catalan Communications.

Printed and bound in Spain by JTV
Dep. L.B. 16.927/88

THIS STORY IS A SEQUEL TO "GODS IN CHAOS", PUBLISHED IN EARLY 1988, AND FOLLOWS UP ON SOME OF THE CHARACTERS... IN PARTICULAR ONE ALCIDE NIKOPOL, STILL IN PARIS TWO YEARS AFTER BEING COMMITTED TO HOLY SAVIOR PSYCHIATRIC CENTER...

THE POLITICAL SITUATION IN THE CITY REMAINS UNCHANGED, AND IT'S NOW FEBRUARY 22, 2025...

SHIT! IT'S NOT STARTING ALL OVER AGAIN?... NOT HIM!...

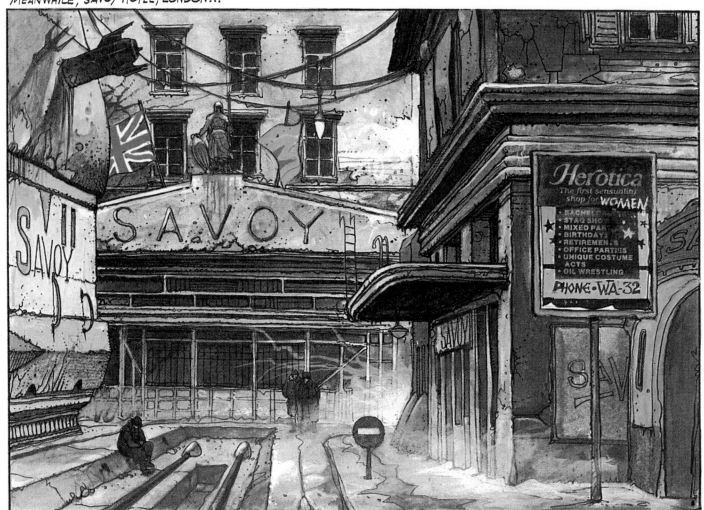

JOHN DIDN'T HAVE TIME TO GET TO ANOTHER PHONE...... DIDN'T EVEN HAVE TIME TO HANG UP........I HEARD THE EXPLOSION........AND HIM SCREAMING........THAT ALPHERATZIAN SCREAM HE LET OUT SOMETIMES WHEN LIGHT HIT HIM, OR, THE FIRST TIMES WE MADE LOVE............

......KILLED IN A ZUBEN'UBIAN ATTACK, ALONG WITH FOUR AFRO-PAKISTANIS, ONE OF WHOM WAS A KEY PLAYER IN THE CONFLICT.... I DECIDE HERE AND NOW NOT TO WRITE ANY MORE ABOUT THIS SYSTEMATIC SLAUGHTER......... I'D MUCH RATHER TALK ABOUT JOHN........AND I'LL DO JUST THAT....... THE SCRIPT-WALKER IS STILL WORKING. JOHN STILL HAS THE PROOF IN HIS HAND...........

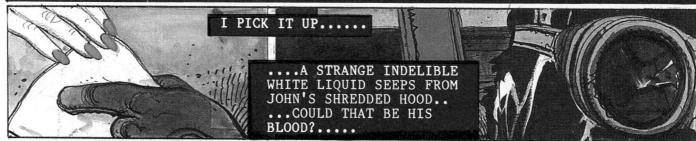

I PICK IT UP.......

....A STRANGE INDELIBLE WHITE LIQUID SEEPS FROM JOHN'S SHREDDED HOOD.. ...COULD THAT BE HIS BLOOD?.....

I HEAD HOME..

BACK AT THE SAVOY I COLLAPSE IN GRIEF. HOW CAN I EXPLAIN WHAT JOHN MEANT
TO ME?... PARADOXICALLY I FEEL A REAL URGE TO WRITE... IMMEDIATELY...WITH
THE SCRIPT-WALKER, SPREAD OUT OUR CRAZY STORY DEEP INTO THE PAST. EMPTY IT
ALL OUT.....HEAD AND HEART.....AND TO FALL ASLEEP TAKE H.L.V., JOHN'S DRUG,
WHICH WILL MAKE ME FORGET HIM AND ERASE HIM ONCE AND FOR ALL..............

IN THE BATHROOM, I FIND THE BOX... H.L.V....I DON'T KNOW WHAT IT STANDS
FOR. NOW I NEVER WILL KNOW. AND I DON'T GIVE A DAMN...................

INSIDE ARE RED
PILLS AND YELLOW
PILLS............

I HESITATE..

...FINALLY I SWALLOW ONE, THEN ANOTHER ONE... BOTH RED... A SPLASH OF WATER AROUND MY EYES TO WIPE AWAY MY BLUE TEARS....

.....THEN, NAKED, I SHUT MYSELF UP WITH THE SCRIPT-WALKER IN JOHN'S ROOM... THE DARK ROOM, NOT A TRACE OF LIGHT.........
... I START TO WRITE... ONCE UPON A TIME JOHN AND I.......

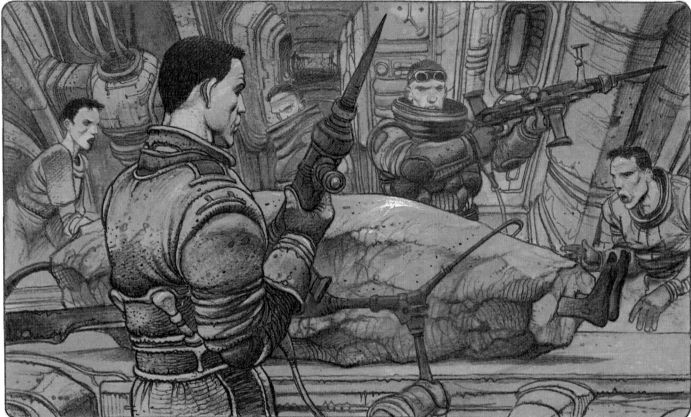

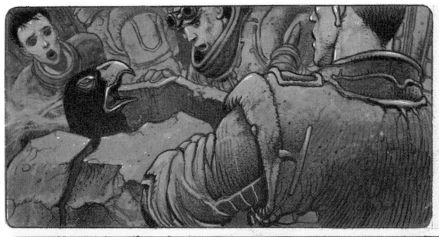

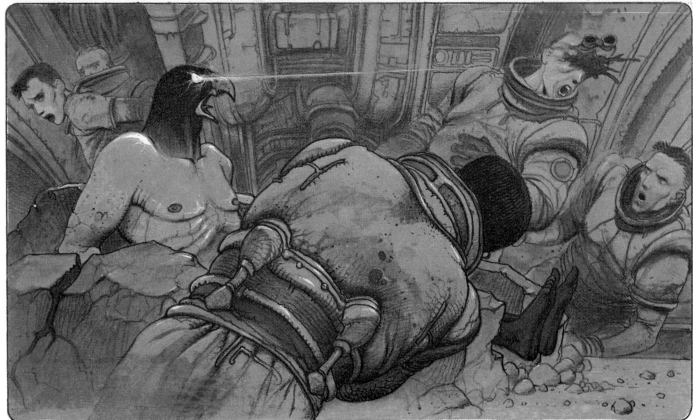

... IDIOTS !!!

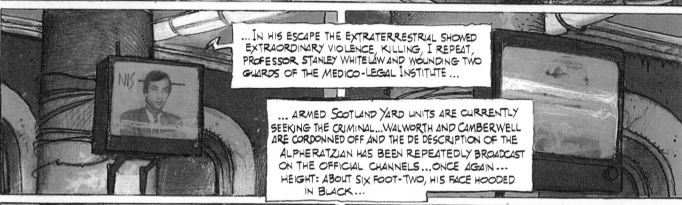

JILL ?!!

...IT'S JEFF, JEFF WYNYATT, WHO WOKE ME 48 HOURS LATER OUT OF WHAT HE INSULT-INGLY CALLS A "DEEP COMA"...
...JEFF IS A FRIEND, A BLACK-LISTED JOURNALIST, A LONELY, CRAZY MAN I ONCE HAD A BRIEF AFFAIR WITH A FEW YEARS AGO (THREE TO BE EXACT), JUST BEFORE I MET JOHN...

...THEN HE DRAGS ME, STILL STONED, TO THE SAVOY RESTAURANT. OUTRAGEOUSLY EXPENSIVE AND VERY BAD, YET I MANAGE TO STUFF MYSELF.....

...DURING DESSERT I ASK HIM:

ARE YOU DOING ALL THIS IN THE HOPE THAT YOU'LL GET TO LAY ME AGAIN, JEFF ?

YOU NEVER KNOW, JILL... FOR NOW THE MOST IMPORTANT THING IS TO FORGET EVERYTHING YOU'VE JUST BEEN THROUGH... JOHN IS DEAD./... YOU'VE GOT TO FORGET HIM... MAKE A BREAK, CLEAR OUT OF THIS LONDON HELL HOLE... SO LISTEN; I'VE GOT A PLAN FOR YOU...

...A PLAN THAT'S BETTER THAN ALL THAT GARBAGE YOU'VE BEEN SWALLOWING...

...WHAT JEFF SUGGESTS IS THAT I LEAVE LONDON...A PRETTY RARE THING THESE DAYS, RESERVED FOR THE KING'S CHOSEN FEW OF WHOM JEFF IS NOT ONE AND ME EVEN LESS SO.....

..."WHEN, HOW, GOING WHERE?" I ASK, A BIT SLOSHED....

..."TOMORROW MORNING, BY AIR-TAXI, TO BERLIN," HE ANSWERS....

... A FRIEND OF MINE, NICK, WILL GO WITH YOU ... I'VE GOT MONEY FOR YOU AND AN ORDER FOR PERMANENT ASSIGNMENT FROM THE N.I.S. ... IT'S PHONY, BUT IT'LL GET YOU OUT OF LONDON... ONCE YOU'RE IN BERLIN YOU'LL STAY AT THE MAUER PALAST...IT'S THE ONLY PRIVATE HOTEL IN TOWN... VERY BEAUTIFUL AND VERY EXPENSIVE... YOU'LL LOVE IT...

... FROM THERE, I'M COUNTING ON YOU TO COVER BERLIN NEWS IN GENERAL WITH A PRIORITY ON THE EUROPA I'S RETURN TO EARTH...

..."EUROPA I" WAS THE FIRST EUROPEAN INTERPLANETARY SPACE MISSION, LAUNCHED IN 1999 (THE YEAR I WAS BORN)....IT SEEMS THEY'RE EXPECTING IT BACK IN A FEW DAYS AT THE BERLIN-TEGEL/TREPTOW ASTROPORT......

... AS FOR ME, I'LL BE LOOKING FOR A WAY TO SELL YOUR STORIES HERE... ...AND IN A WHILE, WHO KNOWS, MAYBE I'LL BE ABLE TO JOIN YOU IN BERLIN.......

...JEFF NEVER SHOULD HAVE UTTERED THAT LAST SENTENCE......

...IT'S CRAZY HOW MUCH BLOOD HE LOSES ONCE I'VE STABBED HIM THROUGH THE HEART WITH THE SCRIPT-WALKER'S DETACHABLE ANTENNA.........FUNNY THING IS I HAVE A HARDER TIME GETTING ALL THE BLOOD OFF MY HANDS AND BODY THAN I DO GETTING RID OF HIS BODY........

...I DECIDE TO GO RIGHT TO SLEEP AND WIPE IT ALL OUT (RED H.L.V. PILL)....

THAT NIGHT, IN PARIS...

FUCKING FLYING SHIT...

... THESE NIGHTMARES APPEAR TO BE REAL, COMRADE NIKOPOL... BUT ALL THE OTHER SYMPTOMS SEEM TO HAVE BEEN FAKED, TO SAY THE LEAST, FOR A LONG TIME NOW... IN OTHER WORDS YOUR FATHER REFUSES TO ADMIT THAT HE'S RECOVERED HIS SANITY...

HE'S COMING, I CAN FEEL IT...

THAT'S RIDICULOUS...

...NOT REALLY... HE'S GONE THROUGH A MAJOR TRAUMA... THIRTY YEARS IN HIBERNATION, PLUS THAT EGYPTIAN GOD (1) STORY, IT LEAVES ITS MARK... IT'S QUITE LOGICAL FOR HIM TO FEEL ALIENATED IN A SOCIETY HE DOES NOT KNOW...ESPECIALLY TOWARD YOU, HIS SON...

WELL, MR. NIKOPOL?

(1) SEE HORUS, "GODS IN CHAOS".

...AND DON'T FORGET COMRADE NIKOPOL, NOT ONLY DO YOU HAVE THE SAME NAME AND LOOK ALIKE, BUT YOU'RE JUST ABOUT THE SAME AGE...

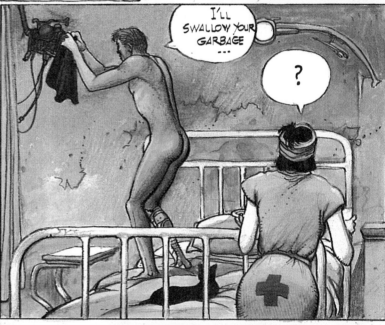

I'LL SWALLOW YOUR GARBAGE...

?

...HAVE YOU HAD ANOTHER NASTY NIGHTMARE ON US.!?!

LOLA, I'VE GOT A DEAL FOR YOU...

...AND IN RETURN YOU'LL FINALLY DO ME THIS LITTLE FAVOR...

MR. NIKOPOL!!!

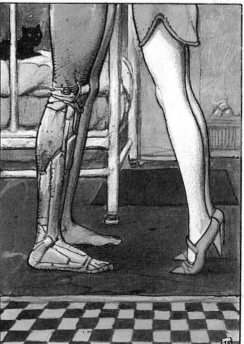

20

...THE GUY ISN'T VERY TALKATIVE...WHICH IS JUST AS WELL...THE EFFECTS OF H.L.V. ON ME AREN'T EXACTLY FLATTERING...ESPECIALLY PHYSICALLY.........
... I HOPE I WON'T THROW UP DURING THE TRIP.......

......FROM A MEMORY STANDPOINT IT'S BLOODY EFFECTIVE.... THE CRIME COMMITTED THAT NIGHT FADES QUICKLY, COLDLY, IN MY HEAD.... JEFF GETS PUT THROUGH THE BUFFING PROCESS AND COMES OUT ERASED...JUST LIKE JOHN......

...FUNNY, THE FACT THAT AN IMPORTANT PART OF MY LIFE (JOHN IN PARTICULAR) HAS BEEN CUT OUT LEAVES ME TOTALLY NUMB..... MAYBE THIS STRANGE FEELING THAT I'M BEING SUCKED FORWARD HAS FILLED UP THE VOID.....SUCKED INTO THE IMMEDIATE FUTURE....MY FUTURE....BERLIN.......

HEY, NICK'S STARTING TO TALK!...

I DON'T ANSWER OR HARDLY..... THE FACT THAT I'M LEAVING LONDON WITH THE CERTAINTY I'LL NEVER BE BACK DOESN'T AFFECT ME ONE LITTLE BIT.....THE CITY'S ALREADY FAR BEHIND...IN RETROSPECT IT SEEMS THAT I HARDLY NOTICE THE COLOR OF THE THAMES AS WE FLY OVER THE RIVER AT TOWER BRIDGE...

...THE THAMES IS RED......

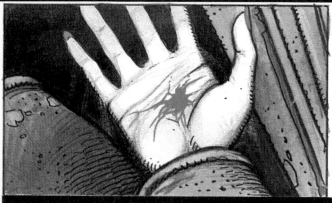

...RED LIKE THE SPOT WHICH HAS JUST APPEARED IN THE PALM OF MY RIGHT HAND...

...IS JEFF'S BLOOD INDELIBLE?...

...I QUICKLY PUT ON A GLOVE TO MAKE IT GO AWAY...IN MY POCKET I STUMBLE ON THE PRESS CLIP JOHN HAD BEEN READING TO ME BEFORE HE DIED....WHAT I DISCOVER IS THE CRUX OF EVERYTHING....

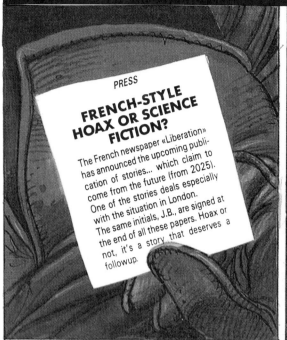

PRESS

FRENCH-STYLE HOAX OR SCIENCE FICTION?

The French newspaper «Liberation» has announced the upcoming publication of stories... which claim to come from the future (from 2025). One of the stories deals especially with the situation in London. The same initials, J.B., are signed at the end of all these papers. Hoax or not, it's a story that deserves a followup.

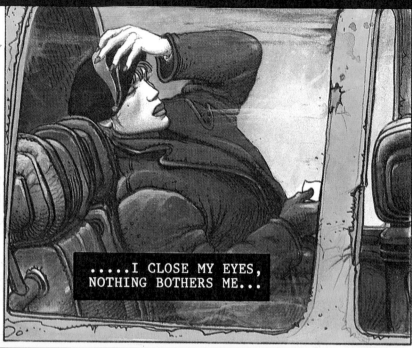

.....I CLOSE MY EYES, NOTHING BOTHERS ME...

...THE PLANE IS ALREADY SOMEWHERE OVER THE CHANNEL...ABOUT TO FLY INTO A HUGE CLOUD MASS (RED)......... I THINK OF WHAT MY READERS FROM 1993 MIGHT LOOK LIKE...HEY, WHY 1993 ANYWAY?...AND WHY A FRENCH NEWSPAPER?........... THE PROGRAMMER MUST HAVE GONE OFF ITS ROCKER....... ANYWAY I DON'T GIVE A DAMN ABOUT THE DATE... THE IMPORTANT THING IS THAT IT WORKS.....................

...BEFORE FALLING ASLEEP, I REALIZE THAT THANKS TO THIS SCRIPT-WALKER I'M DOING THE MOST EXCITING JOURNALISM IN THE WORLD.

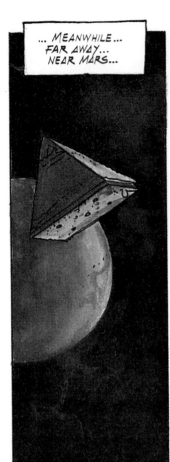

... MEANWHILE... FAR AWAY... NEAR MARS...

YOU'RE SURE HE WAS THERE?

ABSOLUTELY SURE!

BAD NEWS... HORUS HAS DISAPPEARED... FOR AT LEAST A FRACTION OF ETERNITY...PROBABLY DURING A COLLISION WITH A FIELD OF METEORITES...

SO, ARE WE GOING BACK!?

YES, ANUBAST, WE'RE TURNING BACK TO EARTH!

NEAT!

...AT THE END OF THE GREAT RED CLOUD TUNNEL AND AFTER SEVEN HOURS IN FLIGHT THE CITY OF BERLIN FINALLY APPEARS BELOW, THE ONLY AUTONOMOUS ENCLAVE IN THE HEART OF THE CZECHOSOVIET EMPIRE.........

BUCKLE UP!... IT'S A SMALL LANDING FIELD...

...SAYING GOODBYE TO NICK, I FEEL REALLY UNEASY...THE WAY HE SHAKES MY HAND...AND HIS ICY STARE FOLLOWING ME OUT OF SIGHT...A PERVERSE, HORRIBLY PENETRATING STARE...AIMED STRAIGHT AT THE SMALL OF MY BACK.........

ROOM SERVICE? ...

ANXIETY AT TEGEL-TREPTOW...

IT WOULD APPEAR THAT SOMETHING VERY SERIOUS IS ABOUT TO TARNISH THE RETURN OF EUROPA I TO EARTH..... THE BERLIN ASTROPORT AUTHORITIES REFUSE FOR THE MOMENT TO MAKE ANY STATEMENT, BUT DRACONIAN SECURITY MEASURES ARE NOW IN FORCE...
THE LANDING, I REPEAT, IS SCHEDULED IN LESS THAN 48 HOURS...

... I'LL BE THERE...AND IF THERE'S TROUBLE SO MUCH THE BETTER...

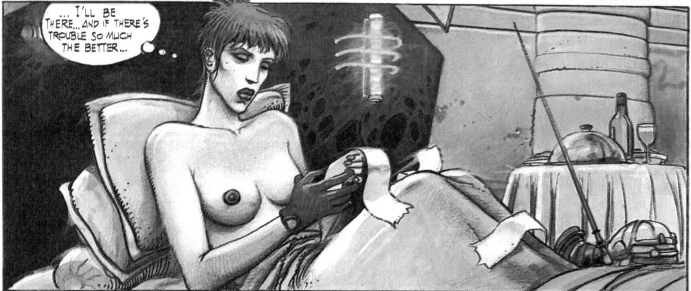

...IT'S NIGHT IN BERLIN...
I'M READING BACK EVERYTHING I TYPED INTO THE SCRIPT-WALKER IN THE ORDER I WROTE IT... "FIGHTING AMONG MINORITIES IN LONDON," FIRST...KIND OF A DRAG...THEN THE STUFF ON JOHN...PRETTY WEIRD... ESPECIALLY IN HINDSIGHT...THE SEX MAKES ME SMILE...AS FOR THE REST, MY FEELINGS AND CONFESSING MY CRIME, I DON'T GIVE IT A THOUGHT... TOMORROW, I'LL BE BACK TO NORMAL WITH A SERIOUS REPORT ON THE MAUER PALAST AND ITS NEIGHBORHOOD...

...I CAN'T GET TO SLEEP...

...AND IT'S JUST AS WELL...THAT BASTARD NICK, SLIMY, DIRTY SNAKE THAT HE IS, MANAGES TO CRAWL UNDER MY SHEETS IN THE DEAD OF NIGHT.....

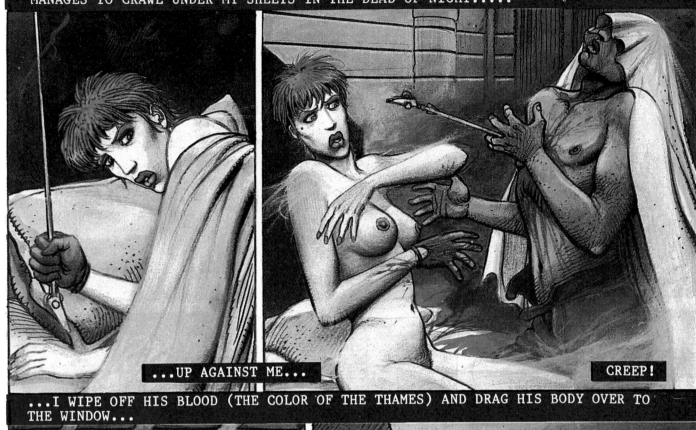

...UP AGAINST ME...

CREEP!

...I WIPE OFF HIS BLOOD (THE COLOR OF THE THAMES) AND DRAG HIS BODY OVER TO THE WINDOW...

..I SHOVE IT OUT...

...NOT A TRACE, ANYWHERE......

...NOT EVEN IN MY HEAD...

...NEXT MORNING, A RUDE AWAKENING...MORTAR AND MACHINE GUN FIRE...

...MOVING IN CLOSE TO THE HOTEL...

CAN I BUY YOU COFFEE?...

...THE ONE TRYING TO PICK ME UP SAYS HIS NAME IS IVAN VABEK, A YUGOSLOVAKIAN REPORTER.......

...JILL BIOSKOP? BIOSKOP MEANS "MOVIE" IN MY LANGUAGE... I DON'T KNOW WHY, BUT IT FITS YOU LIKE A GLOVE...

"OH?!" I LET OUT...
....
....

...SPEAKING OF GLOVES, IT WAS GOOD I CHANGED MINE.. ...RED ONES SEEM TO SOLVE THE PROBLEM.............

...WHILE THE COFFEE IS BURNING DOWN MY THROAT, I CAN'T HELP TOYING WITH THE IDEA OF WHETHER I'D HAVE THE NERVE TO KILL THIS GUY LIKE THE TWO OTHERS...

...MY INDECISION EXCITES ME EVEN MORE BECAUSE I FIND MYSELF PHYSICALLY ATTRACTED TO HIM...

...ALL I REMEMBER ABOUT THE LINE HE DISHES OUT ABOUT THE LANDING OF EUROPA I IS HIS PLAN TO GET INTO THE CONTROL TOWER OF THE ASTROPORT THAT NIGHT... AND HIS ASKING ME OUT TO DINNER TOMORROW.......

...I ACCEPT...JUST THEN A ROCKET EXPLODES RIGHT AGAINST THE HOTEL......

WHAT'S ALL THAT SHOOTING OUT THERE?

THAT'S THE CRAZIEST KIND OF FIGHTING I'VE EVER KNOWN... EVERY REPORTER SHOULD COVER IT AT LEAST ONCE IN HIS CAREER... THE BERLINERS CALL IT "EIERKRIEG"... EGG WAR... IF YOU'RE INTERESTED, I CAN GET YOU A BOX SEAT...

...THAT EVENING BACK IN MY ROOM I DO A PIECE ON THE "EIERKRIEG". IT IS IN FACT THE CRAZIEST, MOST GROTESQUE KIND OF FIGHTING I'VE EVER SEEN... I THINK OF IBRAHIM... HE'S SCARY, BUT I WON'T FORGET HIM...

...THE INDELIBLE RED OF NICK'S BLOOD (MIXED WITH JEFF'S?) IS SPREADING ON MY HAND...IT'S A DRAG.. HAVE TO GET ANOTHER GLOVE...ONE LONGER... AT THE BAR I LEARN THAT THE ASTROPORT IS SEALED AND OFF-LIMITS TO THE PRESS... "SECURITY MEASURE" SAYS A SPOKESMAN. THE REPORTERS RAISE HELL..

...I GO OUT........I WANT TO WALK......

...ANYHOW, STORIES ABOUT ROCKETS HAVE ALWAYS BORED ME STIFF...AND AS FAR AS EUROPA I GOES, I DON'T GIVE A SHIT.....

...LATER THAT NIGHT ITS EAR-SPLITTING ROAR, ALMOST UNBEARABLE, TEARS THROUGH BERLIN'S NIGHT SKY AND GIVES ME A CHANCE TO SCREAM MY GUTS OUT FOR A FEW SECONDS... COMING OUT FROM DEEP INSIDE ME AND LEAVING ME FEELING REALLY GOOD AFTERWARDS.........

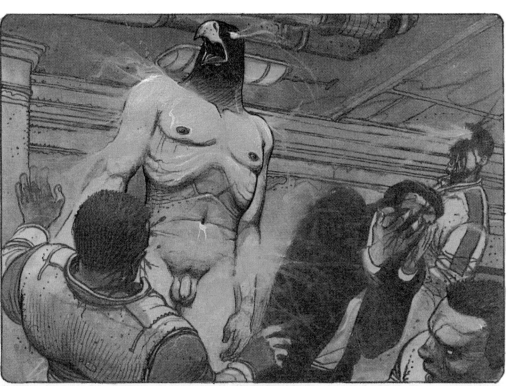

YOU WANT TO SPEAK TO ME, DAD?

YES..

... WHAT I'VE GOT TO SAY IS IMPORTANT... PLEASE DON'T INTERRUPT ME OR CONTRADICT ME... I'LL MAKE IT SHORT...

I'M LISTENING...

HORUS, THE PARANOID GOD, IS BACK ON EARTH... MEETING HIM IS THEREFORE TOTALLY UNAVOIDABLE... TWO POSSIBILITIES... EITHER HE COMES TO ME OR I GO TO HIM...

?

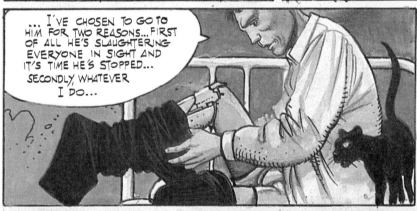

... I'VE CHOSEN TO GO TO HIM FOR TWO REASONS... FIRST OF ALL HE'S SLAUGHTERING EVERYONE IN SIGHT AND IT'S TIME HE'S STOPPED... SECONDLY, WHATEVER I DO...

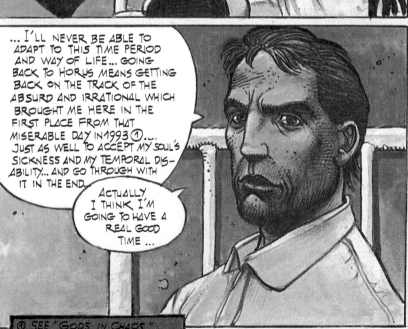

... I'LL NEVER BE ABLE TO ADAPT TO THIS TIME PERIOD AND WAY OF LIFE... GOING BACK TO HORUS MEANS GETTING BACK ON THE TRACK OF THE ABSURD AND IRRATIONAL WHICH BROUGHT ME HERE IN THE FIRST PLACE FROM THAT MISERABLE DAY IN 1993 ①... JUST AS WELL TO ACCEPT MY SOUL'S SICKNESS AND MY TEMPORAL DIS- ABILITY... AND GO THROUGH WITH IT IN THE END...

ACTUALLY I THINK I'M GOING TO HAVE A REAL GOOD TIME...

... THAT'S WHY YOU'RE GOING TO GET A PLANE... FOR ME AND THE CAT, WE'RE LEAVING RIGHT NOW...

...BUT DAD...

① SEE "GODS IN CHAOS".

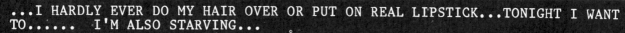
...I HARDLY EVER DO MY HAIR OVER OR PUT ON REAL LIPSTICK...TONIGHT I WANT TO...... I'M ALSO STARVING...

...FORTUNATELY IVAN VABEK IS A PUNCTUAL GUY...

...RIGHT AWAY, IVAN...

...PUNCTUAL, BUT WEIRD......

THERE...

...IT'S TIME TO PUT YOU TO THE TEST, VABEK, ALTHOUGH YOU SEEM ESPECIALLY NERVOUS TO ME...I HOPE YOU WILL BE ABLE TO TAKE MY PRESENCE INSIDE YOUR BODY AND THE INEVITABLE CEREBRAL PRESSURE THAT ENTAILS...

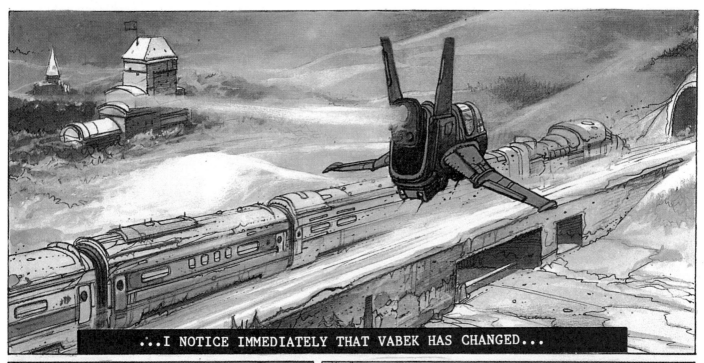

...I NOTICE IMMEDIATELY THAT VABEK HAS CHANGED...

...BUT I CAN'T PUT MY FINGER ON HOW...

...THE FOOD IS AWFUL THAT NIGHT. AND WE HARDLY SPEAK...HE SAYS NOTHING ABOUT EUROPA I. TOTAL BLOCK.... AFTER THE FIRST COURSE HE STARTS SHAKING... HE LEAVES THE TABLE THREE TIMES, KNOCKS OVER HIS GLASS TWICE, AND SMASHES HIS PLATE ONCE WHEN HE CUT HIS MEAT TOO HARD...

...AT DESSERT, HIS NOSE STARTS BLEEDING...

...HE LOSES HIS BALANCE IN MY ROOM WHILE OPENING THE CHAMPAGNE...

...AND THEN, I JUST THINK, HIS MIND...

...I START FEELING SCARED... ..VERY SCARED.

...WHAT HAPPENS THAT NIGHT IS TOTALLY HORRIFYING...I DECIDE TO WRITE ABOUT IT...FOR MY READERS IN 1993.... I RUN TO LOCK MYSELF IN THE BATHROOM WITH THE SCRIPT-WALKER AWAY FROM THE WAVES OF THE THAMES STAINING MY BED... I START TO WRIT.E ... FIRST THE HEADLINE: "HORROR AT THE MAUER PALAST"...

WE'RE HERE, COMRADE NIKOPOL...

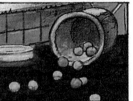

... JEFF NICK AND IVAN...

THESE THREE MAN ARE NAMED JEFF NICK AND IVAN AND THEIR NAMES ARE JEFF NICK AND IVAN   THE FIR ST JEFF   THE SECON NICK THE LAST IVAN THEY'RE JEFF NICK AND IVAN   JECK NIFF AND IVAN   JEN NIVE AND IVAF JIVE NECK AN IFFAN JEFF NICK N IV

... JEFF NICK AND IVAN. JEFFNICKANDIVAN JEFCKNIANDIVANJIFFNECKANDIVAJENF FFNILCKTANJEFFNICKEFF...

... AND JOHN?

46

... HERE, MR. NIKOPOL...
ROOM 412 ...

... IF YOU DON'T
MIND, I'D PREFER
237...

THANK YOU... PUT IT
OVER THERE...

CALM
DOWN, GOGA,
CALM
DOWN...

HORUS.!!?
IT'S NIKOPOL!
I KNOW YOU'RE
HERE!...

I THINK
WE HAVE
SOMETHING
TO TALK
ABOUT...

45

... AND IT'S THANKS TO THIS ANIMAL ACTING AS A KIND OF TELEPATHIC NETWORK THAT I COULD FOLLOW YOUR RETURN TO EARTH...

...I DON'T LIKE CATS... THEY REMIND ME OF BASTET... MY PAST...

EXACTLY!... THE PAST... LET'S CROSS IT OUT! LET'S FORGET IT!!!

POLICE!!! ...FOLLOW US...

... YOU KNOW, HORUS, I'VE GIVEN A LOT OF THOUGHT TO OUR SITUATION AND WHAT OUR RELATIONSHIP COULD BE...

I'M LISTENING...

... IT'S SIMPLE... WE'RE BOTH BECOMING TOTAL LOSERS... EACH IN HIS OWN WAY... YOU ON A DIVINE LEVEL I CAN'T UNDERSTAND AND WHICH IS DRIVING YOU CRAZY, AND ME IN A COMMUNITY OF MEN THAT YOU DESPISE AND THAT TOTALLY OUT OF SYNCH WITH... I FEEL

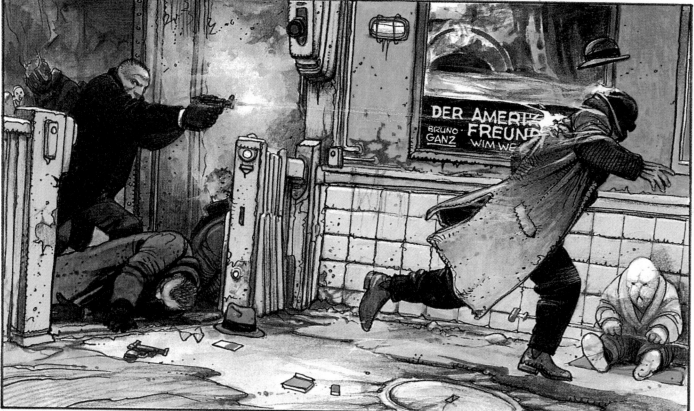

... SO WHAT I'M PROPOSING IS AN ASSOCIATION, NO MORE, NO LESS... ON A TRIAL BASIS... WITH A WELL-DEFINED SET OF RULES... A MORAL CONTRACT IF YOU WILL ... WE'LL GET THROUGH THIS BETTER IF WE COMPLEMENT EACH OTHER... I'M READY TO GIVE YOU A HOME IN MY BODY JUST LIKE BEFORE... YOU KNOW WITH ME THERE WON'T BE ANY REJECTION SYNDROME...

AND WHAT DO YOU WANT IN RETURN?...

49

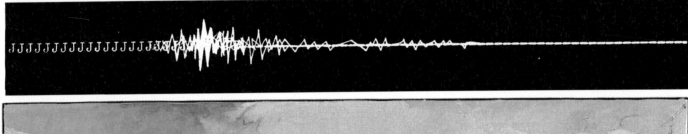

...YOUR HANDS WERE SCRUBBING THAT FABULOUS WHITE BODY OF YOURS OVER AND OVER... YOUR TYPEWRITER WAS ALL JAMMED UP AND STILL SMOKING... I THINK THAT IT WAS RIGHT THEN THAT I FELL IN LOVE WITH YOU... HORUS WAS STUMPED AND I WAS BEWILDERED...

...THAT'S WHEN THE GUY CAME IN... OR RATHER APPEARED, WHO KNOWS HOW... HIS FACE WAS ALL COVERED WITH BLACK GAUZE... THERE WAS SOMETHING TREMENDOUSLY POWERFUL ABOUT HIM... POWERFUL BUT PEACEFUL... HE SAID NOTHING... NO ONE SAID ANYTHING... NOT EVEN HORUS...

... HE WENT RIGHT TO THE PILLS AND BEGAN COUNTING THEM... NINE YELLOW ONES AND TWO REDS... HE TOOK FOUR OF THEM (INCLUDING TWO RED ONES)... JUST MUTTERING IN A HOLLOW, ECHOING VOICE:

WRONG DOSAGE, LITTLE JERK...

... THEN HE TOOK YOU OUT OF THE SHOWER AND MADE YOU SWALLOW THE SEVEN YELLOW ONES THAT WERE LEFT...

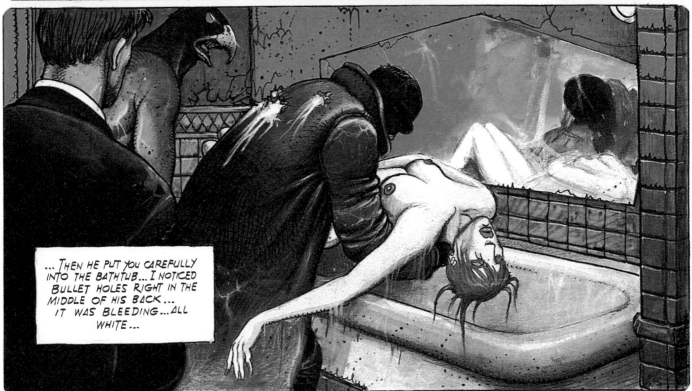

... THEN HE PUT YOU CAREFULLY INTO THE BATHTUB... I NOTICED BULLET HOLES RIGHT IN THE MIDDLE OF HIS BACK... IT WAS BLEEDING... ALL WHITE...

... AFTER KISSING YOU THROUGH THAT WEIRD MASK OF HIS, HE TOOK TWO OF THOSE PILLS HIMSELF (ONE OF EACH COLOR), AND SAID: "THE TWO LEFT OVER ARE FOR HER... SHE MIGHT NEED THEM SOME DAY... FOR ANOTHER STORY."

... THEN HE LEFT THE BATHROOM... AS HE PUT YOUR BERET ON I HEARD HIM MUTTER: "ONE LAST SOUVENIR ..." HORUS AND I WERE TOTAL JERKS. WE DIDN'T UNDERSTAND A THING... IN THE FOLLOWING SECOND HE VANISHED... JUST AS CLEANLY AS HE'D APPEARED...... HIS BACK STILL OOZING ...

... THE CORPSE OF THE UN-FORTUNATE VABEK LYING ON THE BED BROUGHT US BACK TO HARD REALITY...

THEN THINGS STARTED HAPPENING AT A HELLISH PACE, BECAUSE WE HAD TO GET AWAY SOONER THAN WE'D PLANNED DUE TO THE APPEARANCE OF THE PYRAMID OVER BERLIN... YOU WERE IN A DEEP SLEEP WHEN WE LOADED YOUR BODY INTO AN AIR-TAXI WE'D HAD A HARD TIME GETTING AND THEN SPLIT... DUE SOUTH.'... HORUS WASN'T REALLY SURPRISED TO SEE HIS OWN PEOPLE HOT ON HIS TRAIL AND PILOTED LIKE A GOD... GOGOL HAD GOTTEN BACK HIS GREEN AND WHITE STRIPES AND WAS OVERJOYED TO LEAVE EUROPE WHERE THAT EX-TERRORIST HEAD OF HIS STILL HAD A PRICE ON IT... AND ME, ALCIDE NIKOPOL SENIOR (I'LL EXPLAIN THAT SOMEDAY...) ? THE ADVENTURE OF IT TURNED ME ON WHILE I WAITED FOR YOU TO WAKE UP.....

YOU WANTED TO EXPERIENCE THE UNBELIEV-ABLE, NIKOPOL !! AND YOU'RE " GOING TO !!!

51

WAS I ASLEEP A LONG TIME?

PRETTY LONG, YES...BETWEEN THE YELLOW PILLS AND OUR ARRIVAL HERE THAT MAKES ABOUT A HUNDRED HOURS...

HOW DO YOU FEEL?....

I DON'T KNOW... WEIRD...

The day after I woke up --
March 6, 2025
Cairo -- I'm starting a diary...
...Because I need to write even more now...
Nikopol and Horus are beside a swimming-pool with no water... it's hot...
I just read a copy of what I wrote on the Script-Walker and felt totally detached...
    Dead people, "Thames colored" blood (!!!?')... Was I out of my mind?...
    Anyway there isn't a trace of anything on my hands or body, nothing...
    I pick up the phone....

52

On that same March 6, 2025, I burn those sad words, proof of twelve days of what seemed like a never-ending, bloody nightmare... ...Except for Ivan Vabek, killed by Horus (to save me, says he), the others (Jeff and Nick) were dead only in my own mind... And then there's John, much more painful... As I burn the story of our affair, I can feel my stomach sinking, contracting into an open pit, like a gaping wound... But the H.L.V. has cut most of this out my memory, so I'll probably never realize the full extent of the disastrous misunderstanding over his death.... May he live happily without me (he must be immortal), just as I hope to without him...

March 7, 2025 - I've got the feeling I'm starting everything at square one... It's very hot and there's still no water in the pool...

Our sudden departure, due to the appearance of the flying Pyramid over Cairo, was like a game I didn't mind playing at all... That way I didn't have time to ask myself too many questions about how my strange relationship with the Nikopol/Horus pair came about, and even now I don't really know much about it.

KISS ME...

As far as my inclination toward a new love affair is concerned, it would almost scare me if somewhere in the bottom of one of my pockets there weren't those two little pills, especially the _yellow_ one with its spectacular mind-scouring effect...... Already I'm almost happy, it's high noon and we're heading due south, the sun's high, the sand wide open...Farther away still from the cold cities with their wounds and blue tears...